W9-DCW-864

our children

STORIES OF HOPE AND CHANGE

 vitamin angels

PHOTOGRAPHY **Sophia Billikopf & Matt Dayka** INTRODUCTION **Howard B. Schiffer**

ISBN 978-0-692-77648-3

———

Designed by Teresa Fabila
Creative direction by Mary Fearn

Project Manager: Katelyn Harbison
Project Consultant: Jenna Wolff Tovar
Project Team: Jill Agonias, Elysia Cook, Madison Tuttle

———

Printed by Haagen Printing in Santa Barbara, CA, USA
www.vitaminangels.org

PHOTOS BY:

Sophia Billikopf: 17, 18, 22, 25, 42, 44-45, 47, 48, 50, 52, 64, 67, 72, 79, 90-91, 95, 99, 102-103, 104, 106, 110-111, 115, 116, 120

Matt Dayka: 2-3, 6-7, 8-9, 10-11, 12, 13, 14, 15, 16, 20, 21, 24, 26, 29, 30-31, 32, 36, 38, 40-41, 49, 51, 56, 57, 58, 59, 60, 62-63, 65, 66, 68-69, 70, 71, 73, 74, 75, 76-77, 78, 81, 83, 84, 86-87, 88, 89, 92-93, 94, 96-97, 100, 101, 105, 108-109, 112, 113, 114, 118, 119

Paul Miyake: 28, 46, 82, 98, 107

Ghaffar Rabiu: 34-35, 37, 54-55, 80, 85

To everyone who has believed in Vitamin Angels during the past twenty-one years and helped us build this into a truly great global organization, for saying yes to these children and moms, and for your ongoing and long-term commitment to make this world a healthier place, we dedicate this book to you.

And to all the parents we meet who only want a better life for their children, who do whatever they can, often with few resources and in the most difficult conditions, we dedicate this book to you. You are our heroes!

Introduction HOWARD B. SCHIFFER

How do you capture someone's spirit in a photo? How do you get people to let down their guard or capture that magical moment between mother and baby that really is pure love? More than their lenses and equipment, great photographers bring themselves to the shoot.

I've often said that how we do at Vitamin Angels is as important as what we do. Watching Matt and Sophia work, I see the extreme kindness, the respect, and genuine caring that makes their photographs come alive. I've watched each of them patiently wait until the excitement of the 'new' visitors (us) dies down, so they can capture the authenticity we are always looking for. It isn't easy. I've seen Matt do everything from making funny faces to monkey sounds to try to get a baby to laugh. I've seen Sophia wait and wait, gently nurturing the connection she is looking for in a child's eyes.

Our photographs have been an integral part of telling the Vitamin Angels story. While it may seem like a dream job for a photographer, the reality can be sleeping in small, sparse, concrete slab, government 'guest' houses, traveling down bumpy dusty roads for 8-10 hours a day to remote villages (with our fair share of flat tires, and mudslides blocking our way just to keep things interesting), and standing under corrugated overhangs for hours in distant mountain villages, waiting for the rain to stop and the clouds to break so we can get that ideal shot.

Matt and Sophia have hung in there with us and clearly their photographs speak for themselves. We feel lucky to have them as part of the Vitamin Angels family.

Howard

OUR TEAM

BOARD MEMBERS

INTERNATIONAL CONSULTANTS

THE POWER OF VITAMINS

At Vitamin Angels we love helping children and we love traveling the world to connect with those we serve. And it's a good thing we love our work, because we have a huge job in front of us. Hundreds of millions of children are suffering from malnutrition which puts their lives at risk. We've made it our mission to get lifesaving and life changing vitamins to the hardest to reach children and mothers. Vitamins though small in size have enormous impact. They help mothers give birth to vibrant babies. They help children fight infection and disease. And they create hope for a healthier tomorrow. In the most critical situations, vitamins save lives. We are continuously encouraged by the strength and fortitude of the families we meet, despite the incredible challenges they regularly face. We believe the well-being of society is linked to the health and safety of mothers and children.

We believe in the power of vitamins.

Jhon Edison

WITH **MOTHER CECELIA**
FROM **PERU**

————

Shoulder-to-shoulder, we sat with Cecelia on the stone schoolhouse steps of her village in the hills of Peru. At thirty-seven years old, she was a confident mother of six. She smiled freely while rocking back and forth, soothing the infant that slept swaddled on her back.

The baby, Jhon Edison, stirred in his slumber, and Cecelia shifted to help him sleep a bit longer. She told us that the prenatal vitamins helped her to feel stronger with this last pregnancy than with her previous pregnancies, and that Jhon Edison was born larger than his five older siblings. Another meaningful benefit was that Cecelia was able to work during her pregnancy – a critical factor as the family recently took out a loan to buy a home in town.

Through her sacrifice, her children will have career opportunities not available to those who live on the outskirts.

In the field stretching towards the horizon, the backs of workers arched toward the swaying crops. With light in her eyes, Cecelia pointed out her husband among them. Cecelia and her husband met when they were young, and built a life on the rugged hillside together. Both parents work to provide for their six children. While her husband labors in the field and on the Inca Trail, Cecelia proudly serves as a community health worker, or Qhali, as the locals call them. A Qhali holds a position of respect and honor in her village. As a Qhali, she is able to provide basic medical care, advice, and aid to her community. She also helps recommend practices that maintain cleanliness in the home.

Later in the day, we hiked down the steep, wet mountain to visit Cecelia's house. One of her younger daughters was pleased to have visitors. The spirited girl wove among us as we toured the humble hillside home. Cecelia's passion for a tidy space clearly extended to her own house. In the garden, she grew small, orderly rows of spinach and lettuce; in the kitchen, an adobe cabinet sheltered cold goods arranged in a neat row. She pointed out these goods, explaining that the family had to purchase more food this season, as a recent freeze destroyed most of their crops. The goods standing on the shelves were few: potatoes, bagged rice, some canned beans. For nursing moms like Cecelia, prenatal vitamins were the only way she was going to have access to the nutrients she and Jhon Edison needed.

As we complimented her home, we asked about her older children. At this, Cecelia paused. She then explained that her eighteen, sixteen, and thirteen-year-old children live alone in the new home in town that she and her husband recently purchased, so the older children can go to school and have a chance at a better life.

Her youngest children will continue to attend the local primary school, and when they require further education, Cecelia will send them to join their older siblings in town. One day, she hopes to move to the new home so she can live there, too. But for now, she must continue to work here so that her family can afford to pay off the loan. No sorrow shadowed her face as she shared these dreams; instead, her face conveyed the hopeful courage which has enabled her to imagine a better world for her children. ❂

Megha

Megha takes a cool bath outside her home. Her favorite game is hide-and-seek, and she plays it often with her sister. Megha continues to remain healthy since she last received both vitamin A and deworming tablets. Her mother likes to hear the girls laughing around the house, and the family looks forward to a future of joy and vitality.

Vilma

WITH **MOTHER ANA MARIA & SISTER**
FROM **GUATEMALA**

———

Ana Maria invited us into the two-bedroom dwelling she shares with her husband and two daughters in El Barranco, Guatemala. A single lightbulb remained unlit inside their home, as she and her husband lack the financial means to pay for electricity. Similarly, their access to a temazcal–a type of traditional sauna used for bathing–is limited to only once per week, because the wood used to heat the water is too expensive for them to purchase daily.

Their restricted income translates to their diets as well. On a typical day, the family can only afford to eat tortillas and fava beans, which fail to provide proper nutrition and sustenance. Although the family owns chickens, the nutrient-rich eggs must be sold for additional income. The farmland around the home they rent has the potential to grow rich crops, but the owners prohibit them from planting anything in the soil.

...it would be a dream come true for her daughter to receive a greater education...

Such a limited variety of food and nutrients, combined with inadequate hygiene, puts the family, and particularly Ana Maria's three-year-old daughter Vilma, at great risk for illness and disease. As we talked with her mother, Vilma wandered outside to play in the dirt in front of their home. Sunlight glinted off orange tints in her brittle brown hair: a somber reminder of the malnutrition from which she has suffered.

Thankfully, young Vilma is now receiving the vitamins she needs to help her growing body and mind thrive, despite her lack of access to healthy foods. With a stronger immune system, she is better prepared to fight common infections and illnesses that are prevalent in her community.

Ana Maria said it would be a dream come true for her daughter to receive a greater education and to hold a professional job one day. Specifically, she aspires for Vilma to become a teacher and educate others. ✪

Priscilla

WITH **GRANDMOTHER EDINANSI**
FROM **UGANDA**

Edinansi was so convinced of the benefits that her granddaughter, four-year-old Priscilla, received from vitamins and deworming tablets, that she became an advocate for our work in her Ugandan community. This sprightly grandmother now actively shares the power of vitamins with local mothers and helps educate them on the importance of keeping their children healthy. "Prevention is better than having to cure," she told us. Edinansi loves to watch Priscilla move about the home with strength and energy, and can see her one day running a household of her own.

Jamileth

FROM **PANAMA**

———

Seven-month-old Jamileth's mother believes "health is every-thing." The other mothers in her village want healthy futures for their children, too. Although their diet has serious nutritional gaps, the vitamin A, prenatal vitamins, and deworming tablets have given the children improved energy, strength, and relief from illness. More healthy days for these young ones means an opportunity to attend school — an advantage many of their parents did not have as children. Jamileth's mother is right: health is everything. Vitamins have brought these children a chance at a brighter future.

Davie

WITH **MOTHER ELLA**
FROM **MALAWI**

Ella's children, including four-year-old Davie, started receiving vitamins soon after birth. Although their village in Malawi endured a drought that affected the health of many in the previous year, Ella's children are still thriving – they're even ranked in the top two positions in school!

Arsema

WITH **MOTHER MOWORKE**
FROM **ETHIOPIA**

Four-month-old Arsema is a very healthy baby. When asked if her baby ever gets sick, her proud mom, Moworke, gave an emphatic "nothing!" Moworke took prenatals throughout her pregnancy and continues to do so as she is exclusively breastfeeding. Though Arsema is just starting to find her arms and legs, her mom dreams that she will one day complete her education and become a productive person.

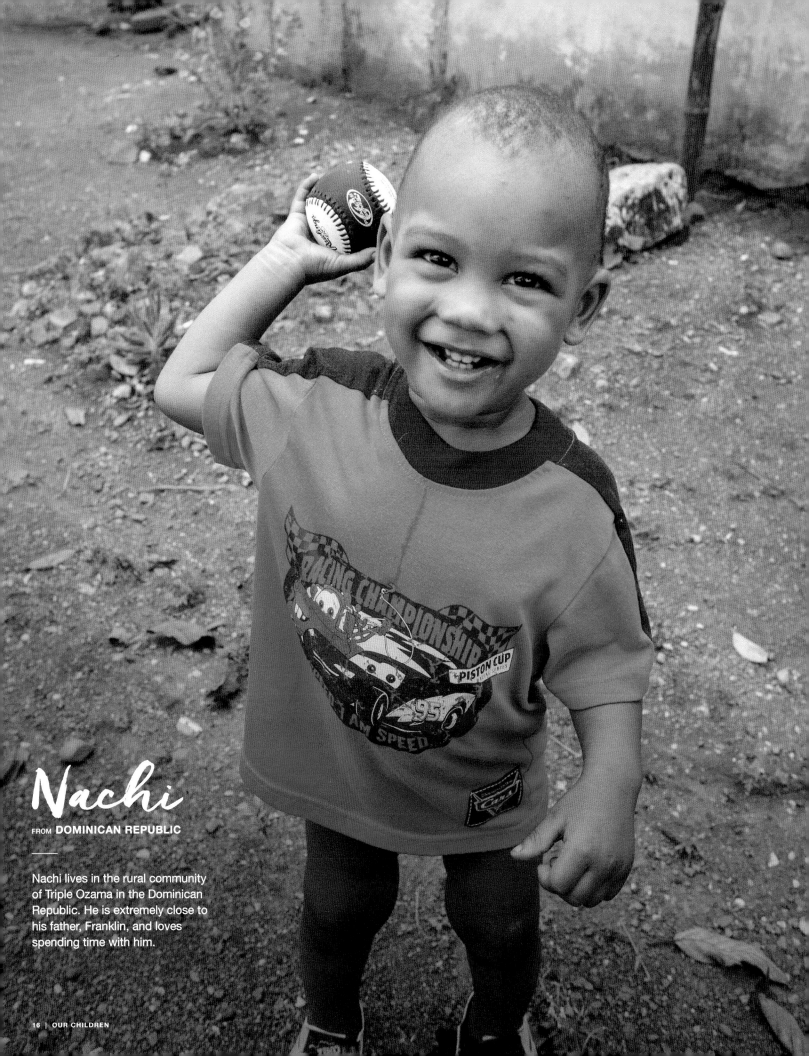

Nachi

FROM DOMINICAN REPUBLIC

Nachi lives in the rural community of Triple Ozama in the Dominican Republic. He is extremely close to his father, Franklin, and loves spending time with him.

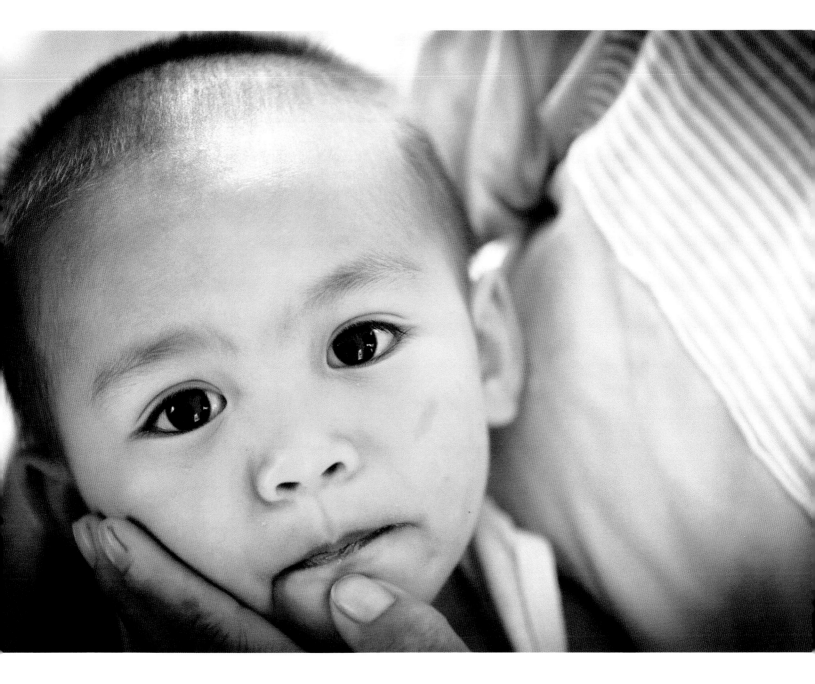

Gabriel

FROM **THE PHILIPPINES**

Two-year-old Gabriel is a shy boy who loves to spend his time curled up in his mother's arms. Without the help of vitamins, Gabriel would not acquire the nutrients he needs to grow. Vitamin A deficiency is categorized as "severe" in the Philippines, which means many other children like Gabriel need supplements from Vitamin Angels.

Kimberly

WITH **MOTHER SANTA**
FROM **GUATEMALA**

According to her mother, Santa, Kimberly spends each day "laughing and learning." She is a friendly little girl with a radiant smile. Kimberly started preschool last year and continues to love her class. Santa is happy that Kimberly got an early start to her education. Santa herself had to drop out of school after 6th grade, as did Kimberly's father, because it was too expensive.

Kimberly and Santa's favorite thing to do together is play school. Kimberly is always the teacher, and loves to teach her mother what she learned in school each day. Santa hopes that Kimberly will grow up to be a teacher because she has an obvious talent for it.

Santa suffers from an unknown illness which makes it impossible for her to work outside the home. However, she recently was able to join her community's weaving cooperative and is now the co-leader! She is thankful to have this opportunity to earn income by weaving bracelets and other jewelry at home, which she later sells through the co-op.

...Santa remembers how Kimberly's belly was swollen from parasites... [and] has noticed a marked improvement in Kimberly's health.

On a typical day, the family eats three meals. Their most common meal is rice, beans, onions, and a local spinach-like green native to the area. They try to eat eggs for breakfast when they can afford them. They also try to purchase potatoes on occasion. They eat fish once per month, more often if there is extra money. Santa told us that if there isn't enough food, Kimberly eats before her parents, so they can be sure she is getting enough.

Her husband, Jose, is a day laborer who mostly finds agricultural work. The work is not steady; some of the time he is without a job. The farms he works on typically grow either onions or flowers, which are sent to the big city to sell. The three of them live in a one-room home attached to Jose's parents' house.

Before starting preschool and getting vitamins, Kimberly was sick much more often. In particular, Santa remembers how Kimberly's belly was swollen from parasites. These parasites caused her pain and gave her diarrhea. She also used to get fevers much more often.

Now, as part of her preschool program, she receives vitamin A, deworming tablets, and a daily multivitamin. Santa has noticed a marked improvement in Kimberly's health. Her belly is no longer swollen, and she doesn't get sick as often. Santa was not able to take prenatals when she was pregnant with Kimberly. The vitamins were too expensive to purchase locally. Cheaper vitamins were available in Panajachel, though the 10-quetzal ($1.30), two-hour round-trip journey was impossible for her to make. Santa feels very strongly that her lack of access to prenatal vitamins caused some of Kimberly's health issues. If she has another child, she is resolved to make it a priority to get prenatals.

Thankfully, prenatals are now available to her through Vitamin Angels' local partner. Santa and her husband are currently waiting to have more children, because they know they need to be in a more stable financial situation before they can afford another child. Right now, she feels happy that she can dedicate all of her attention and resources to Kimberly. Her dream is that Kimberly grows up healthy, continues her education, and learns English. She wants her daughter to have the best life possible. ✪

WITH **MOTHER CHUINH**
FROM **VIETNAM**

For many families in Tsung's Vietnamese community, income is dependent upon the unpredictable weather. Tsung's mom, Chuinh, does her best to supplement the family's daily diet with protein (like eggs) when money is available, but most of the time the family survives on inexpensive rice. Thanks to the advice of a community health worker, Chuinh learned about the availability of vitamin A. She optimistically shared with us that since Tsung started receiving it, he gets sick less frequently.

Jonathan

FROM **PANAMA**

Jonathan hangs out of the window of his parents' small store in San Cristobal, Panama, that is attached to the front of their home. Their store sells basic foods like plantains, yucca, and taro, as well as a lot of processed foods like chips and candy. San Cristobal is a small island off the mainland of Panama, so his mother, Fidelina, travels by boat to the nearest town to buy the goods. Her work is often affected by poor weather and unfortunately, it rains almost 300 days out of the year there.

The weather in San Cristobal also affects what Jonathan's family can grow in their garden. Their diet consists of banana and yucca, which are high in calories but low in nutrients, and sometimes fish. To supplement Jonathan's poor diet, he receives vitamin A and multivitamins. Fidelina says the vitamins will help him grow and increase his appetite. Because tourism is a major source of income in Panama, she hopes that one day Jonathan will be successful in the tourism industry and believes that being healthy will help him get there.

Ernest Adrian

FROM **HONDURAS**

———

Ernest Adrian is five years old and lives in a community on the northern coast of Honduras. Their neighborhood began as a squatter community many years ago, but has since been recognized by the government. Most of the homes in this community are hooked up to electricity and water, which is not the case for many other families in the region who still live in unrecognized communities. Ernest's mom, Wendy, has lived here for twenty-one years, and is very happy that her kids get to grow up in a stable place.

Ernest and his little sister, Elesbi, have been receiving Vitamin Angels' vitamins and deworming tablets through their local school, which is just down the street. Before they started receiving these interventions, Wendy says her children were underweight and had been diagnosed with anemia. She says they always looked pale, had very little appetite, and often had head and stomach pain. After receiving the vitamins, she noticed a big difference in their health and energy levels. They get sick less often and are very energetic.

Now that he is healthier, Ernest is always running around and laughing. He often can be found climbing the big tree in his front yard, and is not afraid to climb all the way to the top! His mom says he has fallen a time or two, but never lets that stop him from climbing right back up. He also loves to play with any newly-hatched chicks from his family's small flock of chickens. Whenever the family has free time, they go to the nearby river to play. Ernest and Elesbi like to splash around in the cool water, because this part of Honduras is very hot and humid! Ernest's mom Wendy is proud to have such happy and energetic children, and she loves watching them grow and play. ✪

Wardin & Maria Altagracia

WITH **MOTHER CLARIBEL**
FROM **DOMINICAN REPUBLIC**

Claribel envisions a future for her children, Wardin and Maria Altagracia, where they have good jobs that make them happy. She is taking night classes to complete her high school education, so that she can help them with their homework and keep them on the path towards success. Before Vitamin Angels' programs arrived in their community, Maria Altagracia and Wardin had suffered from painful intestinal parasites. After they were given deworming tablets and vitamin A, Claribel noticed that both children were more energetic, didn't cry as much, and had much better appetites.

Catarina

FROM **GUATEMALA**

Catarina is a spirited little girl who lives near Panajachel, Guatemala. Her mother brings her in to biweekly meetings to ensure that she is growing properly. This program is specifically designed for children who are considered to be at-risk for malnutrition.

At these workshops, Catarina gets weighed and measured, and receives vitamins and deworming tablets. The program must be working, because Catarina is full of energy and giggles!

Rimpa

FROM **INDIA**

Sabita and her daughter, Rimpa, live a very simple life in Dum Dum Cantonment, India. They share a three-bedroom home with three generations of Sabita's husband's family. Their kitchen is the size of a walk-in closet, in which they cook simple foods like potatoes, rice, and steamed milk with cookies.

In these more traditional villages in India, women stay in the home as the men join the workforce. As a result, women in these areas are often oppressed and have little personal freedom. Understanding that this is a cultural norm, Sabita accepts it and focuses her energy on giving Rimpa a better future.

When Rimpa was born, her weight was extremely low. To make matters worse, she would hardly eat. She seemed listless and didn't cry. Her family feared they would lose her. However, Rimpa has a strength within her, likely fueled by the hope with which her loved ones surrounded her. Thankfully, Rimpa survived and has begun to thrive, thanks to the vitamins and deworming tablets provided by Vitamin Angels. She began taking the supplements a year ago, and she now has a huge appetite and yells for food when she's in a grumpy mood.

The vitamins are essential for supplementing Rimpa's poor diet. At the market, Sabita is only able to buy the cheapest foods, which include potatoes, clarified butter, milk, the occasional fish, and junk foods like cookies. Colorful fruits and vegetables are within arm's reach, but out of their tight budget.

"Every parent wants their child to be healthy"

Food selection isn't a choice for her family; they must survive, so Sabita buys food that is filling though not necessarily nutritious. Almost all of the food they eat lacks vitamin A, which is an essential nutrient for Rimpa's growth. Without this vitamin, the likelihood of Rimpa developing childhood blindness increases significantly. Vitamin A is also vital for a strong immune system that can help Rimpa fight the infections and diseases that are common in her community.

"Every parent wants their child to be healthy," Sabita shared as she reflected on Rimpa's journey to health. The traumatic experience of Rimpa's first few months has led Sabita to understand the importance of nutrition and healthy habits; now, she makes it her mission to bring Rimpa to every possible free health care clinic, including vitamin distributions. ⊙

Danielle

FROM UNITED STATES

—

We met Danielle in Spring Valley, California. She visited our partner's booth to receive her monthly supply of vitamins. She loved the stickers being handed out! Vitamin Angels partners with non-profits all over the United States to provide essential nutrients to children like Danielle.

Meron

WITH **GRANDMOTHER SELENAT**
FROM **ETHIOPIA**

Meron had a delightful glimmer in her eye as she told the Vitamin Angels team how she loved to play an Ethiopian game similar to hopscotch, and that her favorite part of school is art projects with "macaroni!" One day she wants to be a doctor. Her grandmother, Selenat, noted that just a month before, Meron's eye didn't sparkle; rather, it teared constantly and Meron was regularly sick. But 30 days of vitamins made a dramatic impact.

Her eye got better and she is now healthy and has lots of energy. Since Meron began taking vitamins, a new school was built in her village, and Meron loves the lessons that she takes there. In the afternoons, she helps her grandmother care for their family sheep. She has a great sense of humor, and she easily makes Selenat laugh. Selenat looks forward to many more healthy days for her gentle granddaughter.

Shankar

FROM **INDIA**

—

Shankar gave us a cheeky, welcoming grin when we met him and his mother, Raveena, outside their home in Dum Dum Cantonment, India. Shankar does not get the nutrients he needs to grow in his normal diet, but with the help of vitamins, he gets the nutrition his body needs to be healthy.

WITH **MOTHER FLORENCE**
FROM **UGANDA**

_____

For Mutesi and her mother, Florence, reaching a vitamin distribution is not easy. It is a 40-minute trek for Florence in the blazing Ugandan heat, carrying Mutesi on her back in a beautifully bold patterned cloth. The walk is exhausting, especially for someone who has already worked all morning in her garden.

"My joy is my family ... When I look at them, I feel like everything is perfect."

Florence is a small-scale farmer, tending a large plot behind her home. She spends hours there every day, beginning early in the morning and ending when the afternoon sun becomes too hot to bear. The work is back-breaking. Like most farmers in rural East Africa, she does the planting, weeding, hoeing, and harvesting by hand. She has to sell off her most nutritious fruits and vegetables to make a living, earning less than $3 a day.

Florence's salary is all she has to provide for Mutesi's daily needs. They live in a house made of mud, straw, and sticks. The foundation is starting to fall apart. During the powerful rainstorms that plague the grasslands of Uganda, Florence worries that their home will be washed away.

Even with these challenges, Mutesi and Florence are happy, and freely share their smiles. "My joy is my family," she said. "When I look at them, I feel like everything is perfect." Her eyes light up every time she says Mutesi's name.

"My hopes and dreams for Mutesi are that she grows up healthy." This is why Florence makes the long walk to attend vitamin A and deworming distributions. She knows these interventions are critical to Mutesi's health and wellbeing. They are clearly working, because Mutesi is an energetic, friendly girl, loved by all her neighbors. Seeing her laugh, play, and help with gardening, all of which are possible because of her good health, makes Florence smile more than anything else. ✪

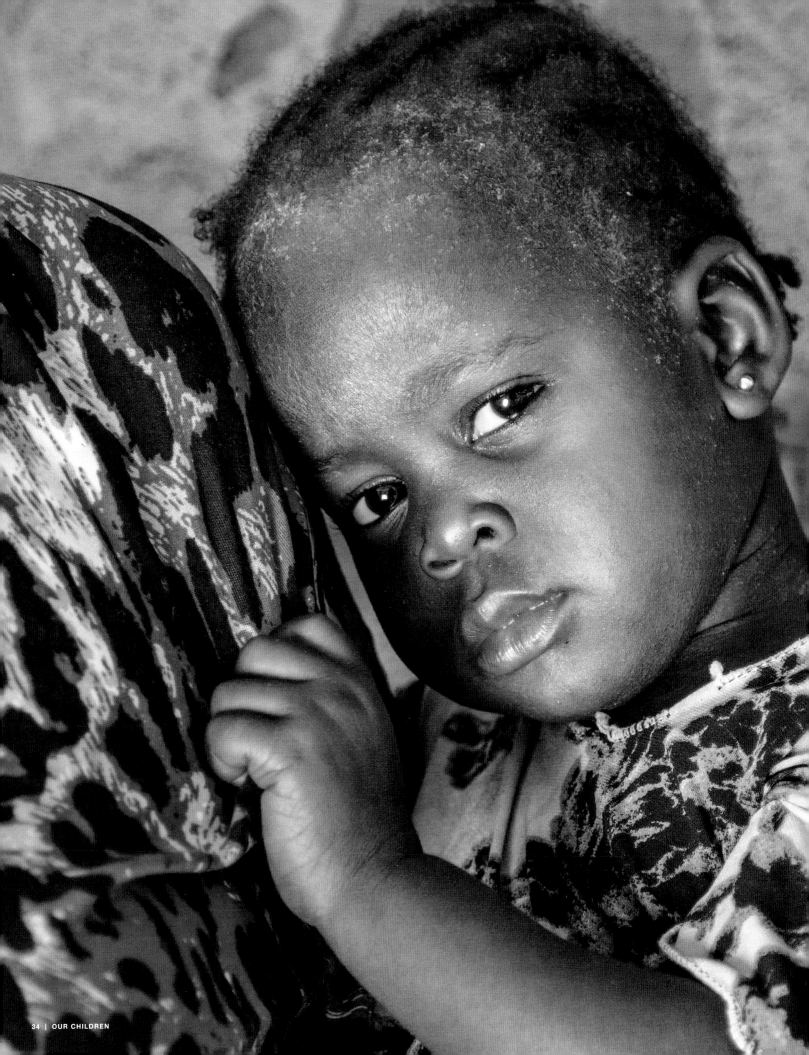

Salaha

FROM **NIGERIA**

Salaha's mother, Zulahi, likes to tell her daughter stories before bedtime. Together they share dreams and imaginary worlds. Zulahi believes that the vitamin supplements provided by Vitamin Angels have helped Salaha not to get sick. As she grows healthy and strong, Salaha will learn to tell stories of her own.

Ana Estela

FROM **GUATEMALA**

Two years after starting to take vitamins, Ana Estela is a completely different child. Once lethargic, she now runs and plays with fervor, grinning and hugging visitors to welcome them. She is even the leader of her class' traditional dance group and loves to show off her talent! Her mother makes sure that Ana Estela regularly receives vitamins at the vitamin distributions in their community, in order to keeping her on a path of good health!

Abdulmalik

WITH **MOTHER ADAMA**
FROM **NIGERIA**

Abdulmalik enjoys playing ball with his friends after school. As they ran in the hot sun, his mother pointed out how much he has grown, attributing his strength to the vitamin supplements he received from the last Vitamin Angels distribution. She looks forward to the next distribution, so Abdulmalik can keep growing tall. She hopes that he will grow healthy and be a successful pilot so one day he can take her around the world.

Elizabeth

FROM **UNITED** **STATES**

Four-year-old Elizabeth lives with her family near San Diego, California. Her mom, Katrina, makes it a point to live as healthy a life as possible. She works as a house cleaner and tries to use all natural products. She is so health and environmentally conscious that she even recycles laundry water! She wants to pass along her knowledge to her daughter, Elizabeth.

Katrina recognizes that the traditional Hispanic diet does not provide a lot of nutrition. On an average night, Katrina and her family used to drink a lot of soda, and eat rice, beans, and red meat. However, after educating herself on the importance of vitamins and nutrients, she realized her family needed to make a lifestyle change. She started to prepare salads with a variety of vegetables and began introducing fish into meals. Katrina then went to seek vitamins to make up for what she and her children might be lacking in their daily meals. Unfortunately, though, the vitamins were expensive and out of her budget. Luckily, she found out that Vitamin Angels distributes vitamins through a local organization in her town, and has now been able to get the supplements her children need free of cost!

Katrina comments that she has loved watching her children grow up. Elizabeth has grown so much in the past year, and is full of energy! Her grandmother always asks, "Why doesn't she ever sit down?" Katrina doesn't mind she knows Elizabeth is healthy. Watching Elizabeth play with her older brother, Katrina notes that the best part about being a mom is getting to see her childrens' smiles. Her eyes light up as she watches Elizabeth giggle at a joke her older brother told.

...after educating herself on the importance of vitamins and nutrients, she realized her family needed to make a lifestyle change.

Even though she sometimes has to explain to Elizabeth why she can't eat certain unhealthy things, Katrina says that Elizabeth is starting to learn. Katrina couldn't be prouder of her daughter for being open to trying healthy foods, and knows she has a bright future ahead of her! ⊘

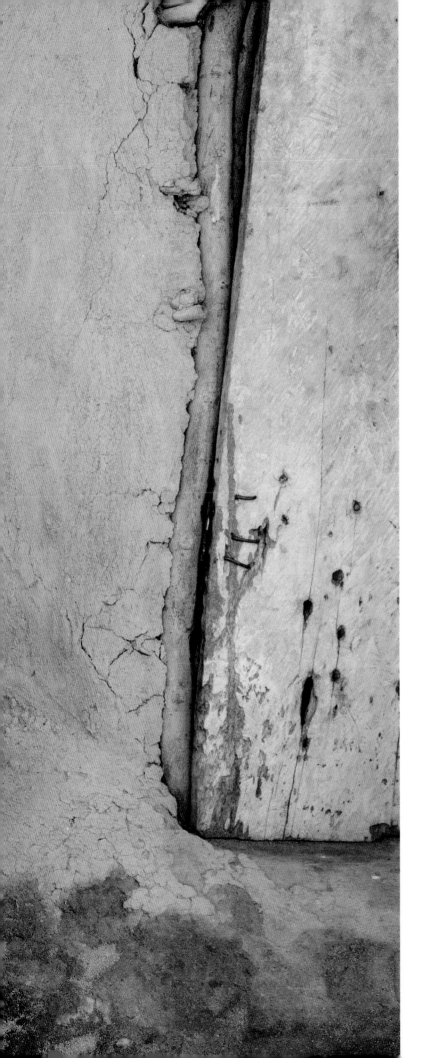

Metrin

WITH MOTHER NANDERA & SISTERS GLORIA & ROSE FROM UGANDA

———

Metrin (pictured far right) is a playful three-year-old girl living on a small island on Lake Victoria in Uganda, where disease is rampant. The vitamin A she has been receiving for the past year has helped boost her immunity to the illnesses prevalent in the area, including measles and diarrhea. It also helps supplement her daily diet that includes cassava and bananas, which are high in calories, but low in nutrients. Her mother, Eveline, says that seeing Metrin play brings her joy, because she knows this means Metrin is healthy.

Jose Eduardo

FROM **EL SALVADOR**

———

Three-year-old Jose Eduardo darted back and forth across his paved yard in El Cedro, El Salvador. We took joy in his easy energy as he showed off his toys. When he heard his mother, Maura, mention to us that he was about to begin school, he sprinted into his home and returned a moment later with his new backpack. He strapped it on and marched proudly before us before opening it up to reveal his new school supplies.

As he emptied the contents of his backpack onto the pavement, Maura shared that Jose Eduardo likes his vitamins so much that he usually asks for more – he said they taste like candy! For a growing boy about to start school, his eagerness to take vitamins is encouraging, for they can help foster strength and endurance as he grows. By staying healthy, he'll be more likely to avoid illness and make the most out of his budding education.

...and they are forced to sell most of what they grow as a source of income.

Maura also candidly observed that ever since he began taking vitamins, Jose Eduardo's had a greater appetite and has displayed palpable, boundless energy. Sure enough, as soon as Jose Eduardo had finished divesting his backpack of its contents, he hopped on his faded blue toy horse and proceeded to send it careening across the concrete. The wheels squeaked and wobbled as he propelled himself forward, laughing merrily.

As we spoke to Maura, Jose Eduardo continued to play and show off his toys. In contrast to his carefree spirit, Maura shared that the living conditions for her and her family are not without their struggles. On a typical day, she wakes up early to do chores and clean. Their home is surrounded by steep, bumpy, unpaved roads. Weekly, she walks these roads to a river to wash the family's clothes. Access to food for meals is a struggle as well; the prevalence of rain makes it difficult to grow crops, and they are forced to sell most of what they grow as a source of income.

Jose Eduardo returned to his horse, and the wheels' repetitive squeak added friendly noise to our conversation. As her son played, Maura shared an unexpected benefit that vitamins have had on their relationship: as a result of Jose Eduardo's newfound energy, she has to spend more time chasing after him. In turn, she has learned how to play with him - a lesson that strengthened their bond as mother and son. That intimate detail was a heartwarming testament not only to the physical benefits of vitamins, but the emotional ones as well. ✆

Genesis & Ariel

FROM **NICARAGUA**

Though they live in difficult conditions in their village next to the dump, the love between siblings Genesis and Ariel is undeniable. Genesis loves protecting her younger sibling, and would do anything for Ariel. The pair are always ready to discover something new together, and since they began taking vitamins, Genesis and Ariel always have the energy to go on adventures with one another.

Tanner

FROM **UNITED STATES**

—

Tanner and his mom braved the hot Southern California sun to attend a community distribution event. The 90-degree temperature didn't stop Tanner from running around from booth to booth, checking out what was being offered at each, including our vitamins!

Zuleyma Amanda

FROM **EL SALVADOR**

Zuleyma Amanda is a very energetic and friendly
five-year-old girl from Guaymango, El Salvador. She
loves to color, play with stickers, and make new friends.
The energy she receives from vitamin A keeps Zuleyma
Amanda very lively and active!

Sonia Leticia

Sonia Leticia is the second youngest of four children. She just turned five, and has been attending the preschool in the community where she lives, in Tierra Linda, Guatemala. Unfortunately, her father passed away two years ago, leaving her mother, Juana, a widow at age twenty-five. This put on a huge strain on the family, both emotionally and financially. Juana works for an onion farmer, cleaning onions for 25 quetzales per day (just over $3).

For meals, the family of five shares two eggs, tortillas, and tomato sauce. To supplement these small meals, Juana relies on school lunches and the vitamins that Sonia Leticia receives at preschool. Vitamins and deworming tablets are absolutely critical in Sonia Leticia's life, in order to keep her healthy. Juana dreams of a better life for her children, and hopes they can grow up healthy, finish their studies, and find good jobs.

Tensay

WITH **MOTHER SARA**
FROM **ETHIOPIA**

—

Tensay rewarded us with an ear-to-ear grin as we chatted with his mother, Sara, about the prenatal vitamins she's been taking. Since she started taking the prenatal vitamins to support her while breastfeeding, she has experienced less fatigue.

Felipe

WITH **MOTHER CECELIA**
FROM **GUATEMALA**

Felipe just learned how to walk on his own. Exploring his newfound freedom, he loves running barefoot around his home in El Barranco, Guatemala.

Shirley

WITH **MOTHER CHRISTINE**
FROM **KENYA**

———

"I couldn't eat anything without soil," Christine told us, referring to a condition, known as pica, that she suffered from before taking Vitamin Angels' prenatals. Because her body was severely deficient in nutrients and minerals at the time, she sought them out by eating soil. Even still, Christine would vomit almost every time she ate. When she started taking the vitamins, though, her appetite for soil disappeared and her health improved. She recently gave birth to a healthy baby named Shirley, who is now seven months old, happy, and healthy!

Heimy

FROM **EL SALVADOR**

In a simple clinic in El Salvador, we met Virginia and her granddaughter, Heimy. Part of a scattering of concrete dwellings in a community known as the Libertad Residencial, this clinic provides medical care and vitamins to the local families.

While we spoke with Virginia, Heimy giggled and played at our feet. Much like any other two-year-old, Heimy loves to play with dolls, pretend to shop, and run to her heart's content. We were surprised to learn that she had been born two months premature: an unfortunately common occurrence for women who do not have access to proper nutrition during pregnancy. Virginia marveled at Heimy's almost-tangible energy and added that, before she began taking vitamins, Heimy wasn't as social and had much less energy. Now, she is able to keep up with her other young family members, who also share Virginia's home.

With eleven people in her home, Virginia works hard to keep her household in order. As the family matriarch, she sets careful expectations to maintain cleanliness, to encourage imaginative play, and to foster mutual respect between family members. While Virginia manages the home, Heimy's mother provides financial support through her job as a waitress. Heimy's father is not present, and the family does not receive economic support from him.

Virginia takes pride in her ability to keep her large household fed. She provides a regular diet of plantains, beans, tortillas, potatoes, cheese, and the occasional chicken for sustenance. Perishable food cannot be kept long, as the family does not have a refrigerator. Without fresh fruit or vegetables, Heimy benefits from vitamins to fill some nutritional gaps. Someday, Virginia hopes Heimy will attend school and enter a profession. To ensure that every member of her family has a healthy future, Virginia hopes to bring all of her grandchildren to the clinic. Through Heimy, she has seen firsthand how life changing proper nutrition can be.

[Virginia] expressed her gratitude for the people who have helped her family. "You are making a difference," she told us.

Heimy turned her bright face toward her grandmother and gave her a grin. Virginia welcomed her granddaughter into her arms, and expressed her gratitude for the people who have helped her family. "You are making a difference," she told us. When we meet healthy children like Heimy, it is a difference we can clearly see. ✪

Mariam

WITH **MOTHER HAUWA**
FROM **NIGERIA**

———

Before she started taking vitamins, Mariam got sick three times a year with malaria and fever. However, since she received vitamin A and deworming tablets, she has not been sick with anything other than a minor cold. Her mother, Hauwa, believes that with good health, Mariam will grow up strong and happy. Her wish for her daughter is to become a businesswoman so she can be able to care financially for her family and community.

Fate & Desta

WITH **MOTHER GENEME**
FROM **ETHIOPIA**

When he's not playing soccer, Desta bounds around his mother's feet, spreading joy and energy through their home. His mother, Geneme, beamed with pride as she shared with us that both children are happy and healthy since they began taking the vitamins provided by Vitamin Angels. For Geneme, keeping her children healthy is the best part of being a mom.

Idaloris

FROM **PANAMA**

—

Idaloris lives on a small island in Panama that has a significant intestinal worm problem. When Idaloris takes the deworming tablets she receives during vitamin distributions in her local community, she feels much better within only a couple of days! Her body is better able to absorb critical nutrients like vitamin A, and as a result, her appetite increases and she has much more energy to play with her friends.

Nargis

WITH **MOTHER** SELMA & SISTERS
FROM **INDIA**

Selma and her daughters live in a home constructed from branches and empty rice bags, perched on a sidewalk between train tracks and a busy street. Their low-nutrient diets of puffed bread and potatoes are simply not enough to sustain healthy growth in the girls. With little access to healthcare or healthy foods, the vitamin A supplements Selma's youngest daughter, Nargis, was able to receive has made a huge impact on her life. Selma believes that the vitamins will help her children grow up strong and healthy, especially as their appetites increase. Selma hopes that Nargis and her sisters will one day become independent and achieve whatever their hearts desire.

Frandel

FROM **DOMINICAN REPUBLIC**

Frandel lives in a batey (migrant housing attached to what used to be a sugar plantation) in the Dominican Republic. His favorite thing to do is play baseball, which is a very popular pastime in the Dominican Republic!

Sonia

WITH **BROTHER RAJ**
FROM **INDIA**

In a slum of Mumbai, Sonia runs across the train tracks. She and her family live in a makeshift shelter near these tracks. Their home is one of dozens along the rails, a whole colony of impoverished homes. Each home lacks a latrine and regular running water. National health services pass over their informal community as if they are invisible.

He tells us he is grateful her future will look a lot different than his own thanks to the power of vitamins.

Their climate is hot and humid. The air sticks to your skin, and Sonia pulls her hair away from her face as she pauses to smile at her seventeen-year-old brother, Raj. Raj was severely vitamin A deficient as a child.

At the time, he had no means of getting this nutrient, which is critical to immune function, vision, skin, and hair. As a result, he was sick all the time. After a particularly severe fever brought on by measles, he forever lost vision in one eye. Partially blind and having been unable to complete his education, his opportunities for employment and a productive future are dim.

His love for Sonia, however, shines back at her as he returns her smile. He tells us he is grateful that her future will look a lot different than his own thanks to the power of vitamins.

Sonia is a healthy, vibrant, and extremely smart four-year-old. She rarely falls ill with much more than a simple cold. As evidenced by her older brother, her story could have been much different without the twice-yearly vitamin A she's been receiving from Vitamin Angels. ✪

Hannington & Peninah

FROM **UGANDA**

———

Eseller confidently told us that despite being pregnant, she feels strong enough to dig in the garden up to the day she goes into labor! Her strength comes from the prenatal vitamins she's taking, to ensure that her baby enters the world healthy. She didn't take any during her previous three pregnancies, and was notably weak. Now that she's aware of the power of vitamins, Eseller's love for her children, including two-year-old Peninah and four-year-old Hannington (both pictured) is reflected in her conscious decision to educate herself and do whatever is necessary for her children's health. For this reason, she takes them to the biannual vitamin A distributions that are hosted at a school near her home. "Any mother feels so happy to have her kids," she told us. Having a healthy pregnancy and healthy children brings her peace of mind.

Elmer Yovani & Juan Carlos

WITH **SIBLINGS**
FROM **GUATEMALA**

Elmer Yovani (bottom row, left), age three, and Juan Carlos (bottom row, center), age four, are from a rural community in Guatemala called El Barranco. They are the youngest of six children- five boys and one girl. They live in a communal home with their mom, grandma, several aunts, and many cousins. They like to play with their siblings and cousins, and especially love to draw. They attend the same nearby preschool, though they are in different classes. At preschool, they get to learn how to read and write, and get free time to play with their friends.

At school, the boys look forward to receiving a snack and lunch, as well as vitamins and deworming tablets. Elmer, in particular, has benefited from these distributions, as he was very malnourished before he started going to preschool. He had no appetite and was lethargic. After starting to take vitamins, his appetite and energy both increased dramatically. His mom is grateful for his energy; now she can hardly get him to sit down for meals because he wants to keep running and playing!

Natnael

WITH **MOTHER ASTER**
FROM **ETHIOPIA**

Aster took prenatal vitamins, which she received from a distribution in her community, for three months of her pregnancy. When she gave birth to Natnael, she was diagnosed with anemia and given more vitamins to take. Now she feels much better and can breastfeed her son.

Missy

FROM **PANAMA**

Missy's typical diet consists of rice, fish, bananas, yucca, and sometimes chicken. Even when her parents can afford it, the market rarely has an assortment of vegetables to choose from, since the terrain they live on isn't ideal for farming. Luckily, the vitamins Missy receives from the vitamin distributions in her Panamanian community help supplement her diet, mitigate any food insecurities she may face, and give her a chance at a healthier future!

Gladys

FROM **GUATEMALA**

Gladys is four years old. She lives in the village of San Antonio, on the shores of Lake Atitlan. She shares her three-room cinderblock house with her mom and two older siblings. Gladys attends the local preschool, where she receives vitamins and deworming tablets along with her classmates. Her favorite thing to do is play with her best friends, Kimberly and Manuela.

All three girls' mothers work in a weaving co-op, making bracelets and other jewelry. This is their families' main source of income, and the money they earn allows them to purchase food and school supplies for their children. Gladys hopes to grow up to be just like her mom!

Shubushnita & Bisoject

WITH **MOTHER SHONDHA**
FROM **INDIA**

———

Shondha is the happiest when she sees her children, Shubushnita and Bisoject healthy and smiling. She believes the vitamin A supplementation and deworming tablets will help them gain weight, prevent night blindness, and increase their appetites. Shondha wasn't able to fulfil her own personal dreams, but she believes she can now dream for her children and their well being.

Noel

Jean's desire for her children is that they will grow up strong and eventually become doctors or nurses, so that they can help others. With that as her inspiration, Jean brought her daughter, Noel, to a distribution in Haiti because she heard that children become stronger when they receive vitamins. Over 65% of children in Haiti are anemic; these vitamin supplements are crucial to their wellbeing.

Dawit

FROM **ETHIOPIA**

Dawit is notably small for his age, but the vitamins he received for the first time while visiting a clinic in Addis Ababa will help support his healthy physical and mental development. His dedicated mom, Mulu, dreams that Dawit will get a good education and job so he can come back and help her one day.

Josue Daniel

WITH **MOTHER PETRONILA**
FROM **GUATEMALA**

———

Josue Daniel is nine months old and lives with his mother and older sister, Manuela, in Tierra Linda, Guatemala. His mother, Petronila, is part of the women's weaving cooperative in their community. When vitamin A distributions are scheduled at Manuela's preschool, all of the younger siblings, including Josue Daniel, are invited to attend and receive a dose!

Zachariah

FROM **UNITED STATES**

Yolanda's son Zachariah was born healthy and full-term, which came as a relief. She credits this success to the fact that she had access to Vitamin Angels' prenatal vitamins through her local food bank. In addition to vitamins, she received nutritional counseling, a supply of healthy foods, and baby supplies through the food bank's program. She thinks this combination of better nutrition and vitamin supplementation gave her more energy than she had in her previous pregnancies, something for which she is extremely grateful.

Amiright & Alvin

WITH **MOTHER OLIVIA**
FROM **UGANDA**

Before taking vitamin A and deworming tablets, Olivia's boys, Amiright and Alvin, regularly suffered from diarrhea. But now "they're back to life," as Olivia described with a broad smile, and they play nonstop!

FROM **ETHIOPIA**

—

Yonas' sweet smile is immediately engaging. But despite his upbeat personality, he's suffered quite a lot of illness – typhoid, tonsil infections, eye infections and pain – in his short two years. The vitamins he received at the clinic on the day of Vitamin Angels' visit will help put him back on the path to health, so he'll have a better chance at growing up to become the doctor or engineer his mom dreams he will be.

Felipe

WITH **MOTHER JUANA**
FROM **PERU**

We stood beside Juana in the local schoolyard, watching dirt clouds billow around the heels of the children as they played ball in the hot Peruvian sun. Juana said that her four-year-old son, Felipe, is much different from her older children, with a high level of energy that she attributes to the vitamins he takes, provided by Vitamin Angels.

Felipe likes to ask Juana about her life, which has been full of positive change recently.

Though Juana has many responsibilities as a leader in her rural Andean community, she spoke most fondly of the afternoons when she is able to sit with Felipe and draw with him in his coloring books. This is one of the few times he slows down, and they talk about their day together. Felipe likes to ask Juana about her life, which has been full of positive change recently.

In an all-male election, Juana was chosen as the first female president of her community. She became an incredible advocate for community health, especially for the children who often suffer from malnutrition. Though it is difficult to grow much in their rural area, she makes sure her children eat what vegetables she can grow. She knows that their diet is clearly not enough, and has decided to lead by example - taking vitamins herself! As a public leader, Juana is determined to continue making positive changes.

Juana is proud of her mountainside community. She is also proud of Felipe's progress in the local kindergarten. She believes that, with improved health conditions, children like Felipe will cease to suffer from malnutrition, diarrhea, and respiratory infections.

With improved health, they can continue their classes as Felipe has been able to do since first receiving his vitamins. One day, perhaps her son will be able to give back to the community and continue her dream of providing healthier, sustainable futures for future generations. ✪

Wesley

FROM **HAITI**

Wesley's mom diligently takes her son to vitamin distributions near their home in Haiti. Before taking vitamins, she shared that Wesley was a sickly and feverish little boy. Now, Wesley plays more, has more energy, and has not had diarrhea since he started taking vitamins.

Martina

FROM **GUATEMALA**

Three-year-old Martina lives in San Antonio, Guatemala. She attends the local preschool, where she receives vitamins and deworming tablets. All the women in Martina's family wear the traditional dress of San Antonio. In Guatemala, many towns have a typical outfit or color scheme that everyone wears, which is a mark of identity and community belonging.

Suhailat

WITH **MOTHER QURRATUL'IAN**
FROM **NIGERIA**

—

Suhailat lives in the village Tunga Maje, Nigeria with her two older sisters and parents. Before receiving vitamin A and deworming tablets, Suhailat got severe cases of diarrhea. In the past few months, though, she has not gotten sick at all! Her mother hopes, one day, Suhailat will become a teacher in their community.

Daug

FROM **VIETNAM**

Prior to taking vitamins, Daug caught many colds and fevers, and even had hand, foot, and mouth disease. Once his mother, Auh, heard about Vitamin Angels and the benefits of vitamin A from other women in her village, she made sure to bring her son to the next distribution. Since his first vitamin A dose, Daug is noticeably more energetic, and Auh now knows firsthand the power of vitamins.

Kamyrah & Kenadi

FROM **UNITED STATES**

Vitamin Angels' vitamins are distributed every year at the back-to-school event hosted at the local library in Spring Valley, California. Kamyrah and Kenadi's dad brought them to get everything they need for the upcoming school year, including new backpacks, school supplies, and vitamins. Kamyrah will be starting kindergarten soon!

Shonelidas

WITH **MOTHER RUMIDA**
FROM **INDIA**

—

Rumida attributes the health of her vibrant baby, Shonelidas, to both prenatal vitamins and breastfeeding. The prenatals help keep Rumida strong and allow her to pass on necessary nutrients to Shonelidas.

Beau

WITH **MOTHER ASHLEY**
FROM **UNITED STATES**

Beau is a member of the Sioux Tribe in South Dakota. He has lived on the Cheyenne River Sioux Reservation his whole life, as has his mother. He has two older siblings, and is looking forward to becoming a big brother soon! His mom, Ashley, is taking prenatal vitamins to ensure that Beau's little brother or sister has the best chance at a healthy life.

Ibrahim

WITH **MOTHER KHADIJAH**
FROM **NIGERIA**

———

Ibrahim has started preschool in his village Tunga Maje, Nigeria. He used to get sick four times a year but since receiving vitamin A and deworming tablets, he has only been sick once. His mother, Khadijah, believes health is important for him to grow up to become a great man. Ideally, she would like Ibrahim to become a lawyer so he can fight on behalf of their community members for justice.

Edwin

WITH **MOTHER**
FROM **PERU**

———

Edwin's vibrantly colored clothing reflects how bright his future is! He has been receiving vitamins from a distribution in Peru since he was six months old, and has only been sick once since birth.

Getsemani

FROM **UNITED STATES**

Getsemani loves to play with dolls and stuffed animals. She is bilingual in English and Spanish. Getsemani has been receiving vitamins from the food bank near her home. Her mom was so inspired by the positive effects of vitamins and nutritious foods that she started volunteering at the food bank!

Livingstone & Laston

WITH **MOTHER SMALI & FATHER SIMON**
FROM **UGANDA**

Simon's love for his children, Livingstone and Laston, is obvious. He looks at them with admiration and hope and loves the photo of them that was just given to him. Since he can't afford to buy toys, he builds them himself out of metal scraps and wood. Best of all, he makes the toys with certain intentions, like to help his children learn how to walk. "I love my family so much... I want them to be healthy," Simon says, as he notes the importance of vitamins and deworming tablets.

Karen

FROM **GUATEMALA**

Four-year-old Karen lives in El Barranco, a remote agricultural community in the highlands of Guatemala. She lives with her parents and older brother, Daniel. Karen is a vivacious, energetic girl, and even her brother sometimes gets tired trying to keep up with her! The two of them are very close, and Daniel takes his role of "protective big brother" very seriously.

Karen's mother, Rosa, works in a tortilleria, making and selling tortillas, and her father, Carlos, is a farmer. Between the two of them, they make enough money to cover their basic needs, but not enough to cover any unexpected expenses or emergencies. Rosa says the hardest challenge she faces as a mother is not having enough money to buy medicine or take her kids to the hospital if they get sick. Still, she knows many families in her community have even fewer resources, so she feels lucky that she is able to provide food and clothes for her family.

Rosa knows that Karen's good health is vital for achieving her goals in life.

Rosa is very proud that Karen is doing well in preschool. Rosa feels personally responsible for making sure both of her children do well in school, because her husband is always busy working. She believes that school is essential for Karen's future success. Many girls in these communities in the area drop out of school early, to get married or to go to work. Rosa hopes that Karen will graduate and grow up to be a doctor or nurse so that she can help her family and the community.

Rosa knows that Karen's good health is vital for achieving her goals in life. She is very grateful that Karen receives vitamins through the preschool she attends. She says that Karen gets sick much less often, and Rosa has even noticed a difference in the health of her neighbors' children after they started taking vitamins too. In communities like this, vitamins are essential to helping children like Karen grow up healthy! ❂

Jordi & Roy

FROM **PERU**

Yovana lives with her two sons in the high Andes mountains of Peru in the community of Ttio Grande. When she was pregnant with her younger son, Jordi, Yovana took prenatal vitamins. She felt much stronger during her pregnancy and labor, and Jordi was born at a healthy weight of over three kilograms (6 1/2 pounds), which is much heavier than Roy had been at birth.

Cristina

WITH **MOTHER ANABELLA**
FROM **UNITED STATES**

Cristina is two years old, and lives in Southern California. She has a sister, Filyanie, who is four years old. Their mom, Anabella, brings them to the local food bank, where, in addition to food and vitamins, the girls sometimes get toys. They are always happy when they get to pick out a stuffed animal!

Francisca

WITH **BROTHER JUSTO**
FROM **NICARAGUA**

—

Francisca and her older brother, Justo, live in Tipitapa, Nicaragua. They love to hug each other. Justo clearly likes taking care of his sister. In Nicaragua, 23% of children are stunted. Access to vitamins is helping children like Francisca grow up to reach their full potential.

Sarah

FROM **UGANDA**

———

Before receiving the vitamin supplements and deworming tablets provided by Vitamin Angels, Sarah was regularly ill. But now, she is much healthier. In the afternoons, Sarah helps her mother, Kauma, with housework while she shares stories about her school day and draws pictures of her friends, homes, and the local flowers.

Liam

FROM **UNITED STATES**

Liam received vitamins at a community event in Southern California, which he attended with his mom, Sharii, and his big brother, Charles. He hammed it up for the camera, leaving everyone doubled over with laughter!

Junelson

WITH **GRANDFATHER MANDY**
FROM **HAITI**

Junelson lives in Macaco, Haiti with his family.
He especially loves spending time with his grandfather, Mandy. Junelson loves to copy everything
his grandfather does, and Mandy is proud that he
can pass down his knowledge to his grandson.

Leonel Mesi

WITH **MOTHER REYNA**
FROM **PERU**

———

Five-month-old Leonel Mesi (named for the famous soccer player!) loves being rocked to sleep by his mother, Reyna. With the help of vitamins, Reyna knows that one day Leonel will grow too big to fit in her arms, so for now she rests easy watching her son sleep peacefully in her arms.

Sagantika & Sanehita

FROM **INDIA**

Sagantika and Sanehita love causing trouble together near their home in India. Both of their families love watching the boys run up and down the alleyways near their home, as it means they have the energy they need to continue to grow up healthy.

Ysis

FROM **HONDURAS**

—

Two-year-old Ysis is the youngest of four children. When Ysis was only a few months old, her older brother Jose David got terribly sick. He had to stay in the hospital for three months, which drained the family both financially and emotionally. Luckily, Jose David recovered and is back at home. After this unfortunate experience, their mom, Pati, is even more determined to keep her children healthy. She takes Ysis to the local school every six months to get a dose of vitamin A and a deworming tablet. She is so grateful for these interventions because she knows they help to keep Ysis' body and immune system strong and healthy.

FROM THE PHILIPPINES

Vince lives in the Philippines, where snack foods, like the ones pictured here, are often cheaper than fresher, more nutritious alternatives. Families often have to choose quantity over quality, which leaves children susceptible to malnutrition. Luckily, Vitamin Angels is providing essential vitamins to children like Vince throughout the Philippines!

Hasan
WITH MOTHER MARIAM
FROM UGANDA

Hasan lives in a roadside community near Iganga, Uganda. He loves to spend time with his mother, and often watches her while she prepares food. Here, he watches her preparing locally-grown greens, which will be sautéed and eaten with posho (a cornmeal porridge that is a staple in East Africa, also known as ugali or nsima).

Wendy

WITH **MOTHER ROSA MARIA**
FROM **GUATEMALA**

Rosa Maria always makes sure to bring her daughter, Wendy, to vitamin distributions near their home in El Barranco, Guatemala. Wendy loves receiving her vitamin A, but especially loves getting her height measured by the staff at the distribution! Guatemala has one of the highest rates of stunting (children small for their age) in the world, something Vitamin Angels is combatting through the distribution of essential nutrients.

Michael

FROM **UNITED STATES**

Michael loves to color, and proudly shows off each piece of artwork to everyone around. We met him and his mom, Denise, at an all-day distribution event near San Diego, California. They came for the vitamins, but stayed for the fun coloring pages!

Solomon

WITH **MOTHER MESAYE**
FROM **ETHIOPIA**

———

Mesaye sat in the courtyard of the Ziway healthcare clinic where she had come to receive care for herself and vitamins for her little boy, Solomon.

She was so young. At only nineteen years old it seemed as if she had lived more than anyone almost twice her age. Soloman sat shyly in his mom's lap watching the group of people around him. Mesaye shared that she ate three meals a day, but these meals mostly consisted of cabbage or other vegetables. She wore a tattered shirt, which clung to her skin and emphasized her thin frame. With a resigned tone, Mesaye shared that she was a commercial sex worker.

Her hardships are heavy, but Mesaye's strength and resilience never falter

Mesaye's eyes lit up as she turned her attention to Solomon. The two-year-old eagerly engaged with the world around him. Mesaye laughed as she shared how he recently started talking, and talking, and talking all the time. But his loving mother didn't seem to mind. She was glad for tangible evidence of his improved health, thanks to the vitamins he had begun to receive.

Six months before, Solomon wouldn't eat. He had GI trouble and regular diarrhea. Since he began taking vitamins, Mesaye said that his appetite had returned, and his diarrhea went away. He was now healthy and growing strong. Before the vitamins, Solomon was more prone to falling seriously ill because of his poor diet; malnutrition perpetuated the problem. It is an incredible relief to Mesaye that her son is healthy now.

While Solomon and Mesaye crouched on the floor drawing together, the love they shared was apparent. Her hardships are heavy, but Mesaye's strength and resilience never falter. ✪

Franklin

WITH SISTERS MARIA & GENESIS & COUSIN JULI FROM HONDURAS

—

Three-year-old Franklin has two older sisters and one younger sister. The children live with their parents in a hand-built house on the side of a steep hill. Their father works as a trash collector for the city, a steady job that is common in Los Laureles. Unfortunately, though, employees sometimes go months at a time without receiving their salary. Franklin's dad hasn't been paid in four months, which has put a huge financial strain on the family. Franklin's mom says that the lack of income means that some days they don't have enough money for food, making the vitamins Franklin receives even more important for maintaining his health.

WITH **MOTHER** **MESERI**
FROM **ETHIOPIA**

Feeding Negat brings her mother, Meseri, great joy. Negat is growing in energy and strength, and Meseri says that her daughter's increased appetite is directly related to the vitamins she takes.

Mohammed & Sakina

WITH **MOTHER SULTANA**
FROM **INDIA**

———

Sultana is only able to feed her family basic
foods like bread and potatoes, so vitamins
from distributions in their local community are
invaluable. She knows how important it is to
supplement the diets of her children, Mohammad
and Sakina, and believes that vitamins are a real
game changer. Sultana would love for her children
to continue their studies and become teachers
when they are older – she believes it is important
that her children give back to their community
when they grow up.

Jessica

WITH MOTHER AGNES & BROTHERS LEVIS, DANIEL & EMMANUEL
FROM KENYA

At seven months old, Jessica is healthier than her older brothers who have suffered from malaria, anemia, and other health issues throughout much of their young lives. Agnes, Jessica's mother, understands the importance of making sure Jessica receives vitamins from the distributions in Kenya – the differences between her and her older siblings made that clear.

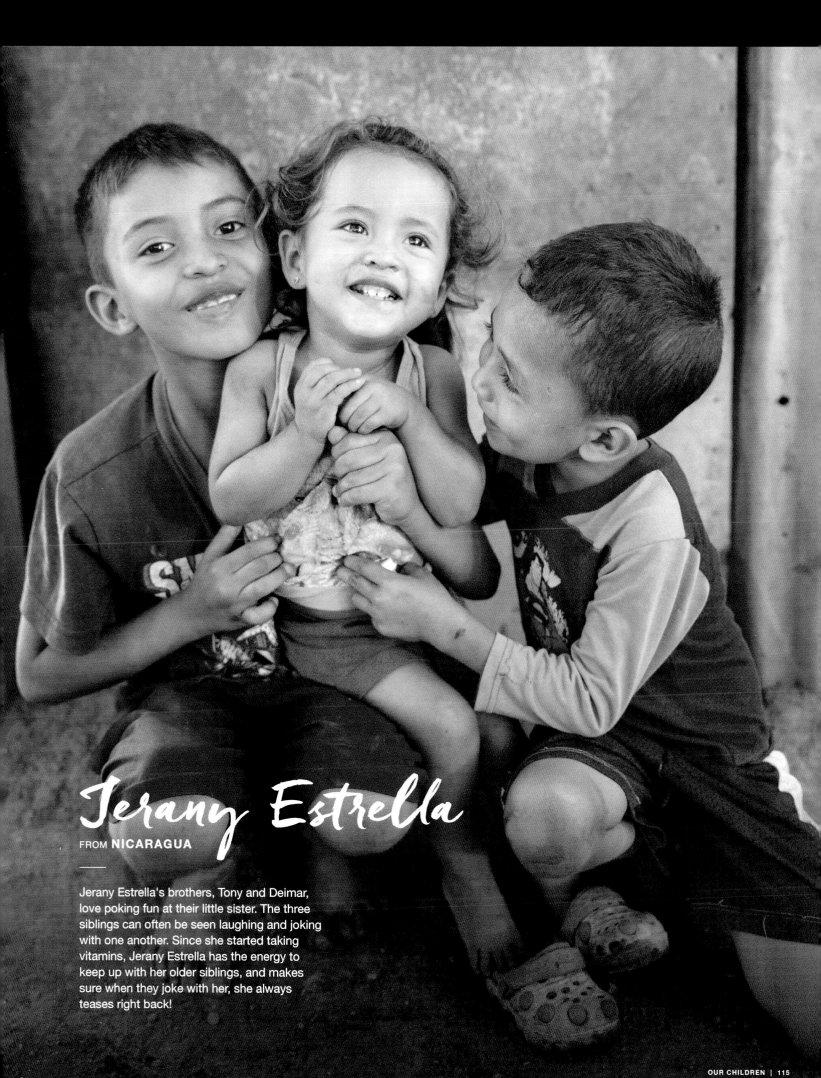

Jerany Estrella

FROM **NICARAGUA**

Jerany Estrella's brothers, Tony and Deimar, love poking fun at their little sister. The three siblings can often be seen laughing and joking with one another. Since she started taking vitamins, Jerany Estrella has the energy to keep up with her older siblings, and makes sure when they joke with her, she always teases right back!

Dahlia & Kimberli

FROM **EL SALVADOR**

A mother's affection and pride radiated from Sandra's face as she watched her two young daughters, Dahlia and Kimberli, play together in Bebedero, El Salvador. The sisters literally horsed around with each other, sharing a stuffed horse doll that their older brother had recently won at a fair for Dahlia.

Sandra instinctively kept an eye on her daughters as she talked to us. As a mother of five, she said that she never feels alone with all of her children around her. She shared that parenting certainly comes with its stresses and challenges, especially considering her family's extremely limited income (her husband works at a gas station). Regardless, she truly enjoys being a mother.

The vitamins they receive help make up for any lack of nutrients in their diets.

A deliberate focus on her family helps Sandra set aside her worries, whether that be drawing on a notebook and letting her daughters color the pictures she creates (one of their favorite pastimes), making them breakfast and dropping them off at school, ensuring that they all take their vitamins, or simply watching them play, as she did while talking to us.

As we spoke to Sandra, both of her girls were notably animated and energetic, a reflection of the benefits their mother received from taking vitamins herself. She happily told us that thanks to the combination of prenatal vitamins during her pregnancies, and vitamins for all five of her children throughout their lives, her children are bigger and more mentally alert than other children in their area.

She credits her family's health to vitamins and a strict adherence to general hygienic practices, like washing one's hands after eating, thoroughly cleaning dishes, avoiding mosquitoes, and staying away from standing water. She learned and adopted those essential tips from the health center in her community. Her and her husband's efforts are not in vain; their children's health and vivacity are testaments to their parents' dedication and sacrifice.

Though the backyard in their home is too small to keep a garden, Sandra likes to cook with the foods she has available. The vitamins they receive help make up for any lack of nutrients in their diets. At the end of every day, the family shares dinner together (fish is the unanimous meal of choice when it's available); it's their way of coming together and connecting after being apart during the day.

Despite the comfort she feels from her children's presence, Sandra's dreams for her children involve them leaving home eventually. Her greatest gift would be for her children to have it all: for her daughters to attend university and for her sons to finish their studies and find good jobs. Though she's unsure if they will have the resources to continue their education, she knows that her children have the health they need to succeed, even if the financial resources to accomplish their goals are not guaranteed. For any mother, raising healthy and happy children is an accomplishment in itself; for families like Sandra's, who face daily challenges to stay healthy and thriving, such an achievement is monumental. ❂

WITH **MOTHER DAMARIS**
FROM **PANAMA**

Damaris' love for her daughter, Yaliky, was evident before she was born. To ensure that Yaliky was born healthy, Damaris made sure to take prenatal vitamins while she was pregnant. She was thrilled that Yaliky was born healthy, weighing in at an impressive nine pounds! Now that she is old enough, Yaliky has begun receiving vitamins, and her mother is hopeful that they will help Yaliky have a better, healthier life.

Tithi

WITH **MOTHER RINKU** FROM **INDIA**

Tithi and her mother, Rinku, stand outside their home in Dasnagar, India. Rinku loves her daughter deeply, and would give anything to see her daughter achieve her dreams. This is why Rinku makes sure Tithi attends vitamin distributions, so she can see her daughter grow up healthy and strong.

Measuring *Success*

Thanks to the generous support of field partners, companies, and individuals, we just had our most successful year ever.

OVER 48 MILLION
children under five, new moms, and pregnant women served.

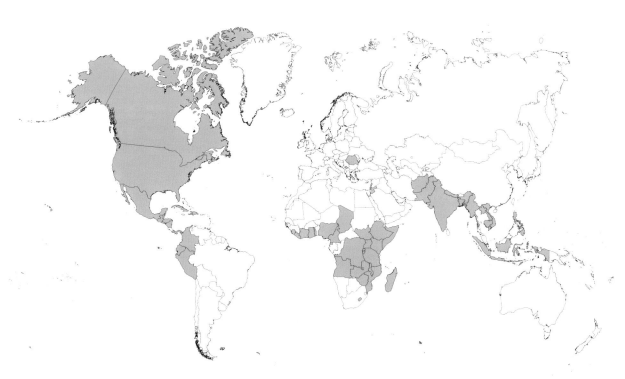

WE WORK IN 1 IN 4 COUNTRIES

WORLDWIDE

74%

Of the 54 countries where Vitamin Angels works, 74% are classified as experiencing moderate, severe or alarmingly high malnutrition.*

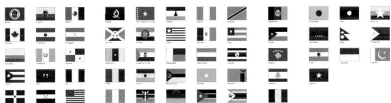

Vitamin A   Multivitamin

Prenatal   Deworming

+230 MILLION
doses distributed

Over 230 million of life changing vitamin A, prenatal and children's multivitamins, and deworming tablets were distributed.

PARTNERED WITH

OVER 800
LOCAL NONPROFITS

that added our vitamins to their existing programs for populations without access to national health services.

*Ruel-Bergeron JC, Stevens GA, Sugimoto JD, Roos FF, Ezzati M, Black RE, et al. (2015) Global Update and Trends of Hidden Hunger, 1995-2011: The Hidden Hunger Index. PLoS ONE 10(12): e0143497.